Barbie™

MY SECRET JOURNAL

This book belongs to:

....

Stick a photo of
yourself in the frame!

centum

MY FAB LIFE

My friends and I want to know all about you, especially all your super-fun secret stuff. Answer these questions so we can find out about your fab life!

Name: ....

Favourite Nickname: ....

Hair Colour: ....

Eye Colour: ....

Cool!

Birthday: ....

Age: ....

Lucky Number: ....

Favourite Time of Year: ....

Most Fabulous Achievement: ....

Best Talent: ....

Worst Habit: ....

Most Embarrassing Moment: ....

Favourite Colour: ....

Favourite Music: ....

Favourite Film Star: ....

Best Look: ....

OMG!

Best Friends: ....

Secret Crush: ....

Cutest Pet: ....

Other Fab Information: ....

....

PICTURE PERFECT

Ready for a close-up? We've stuck in some cool pictures of us. Stick your photos in the fab frames below.

Me with my BFFs

Me as a baby

Your hair looks fabulous!

Super-glam and on the go!

Me on holiday

Chilling out at home

SECRETS

All your secrets are safe with me!

My biggest secret ever:

My secret wish
for this year:

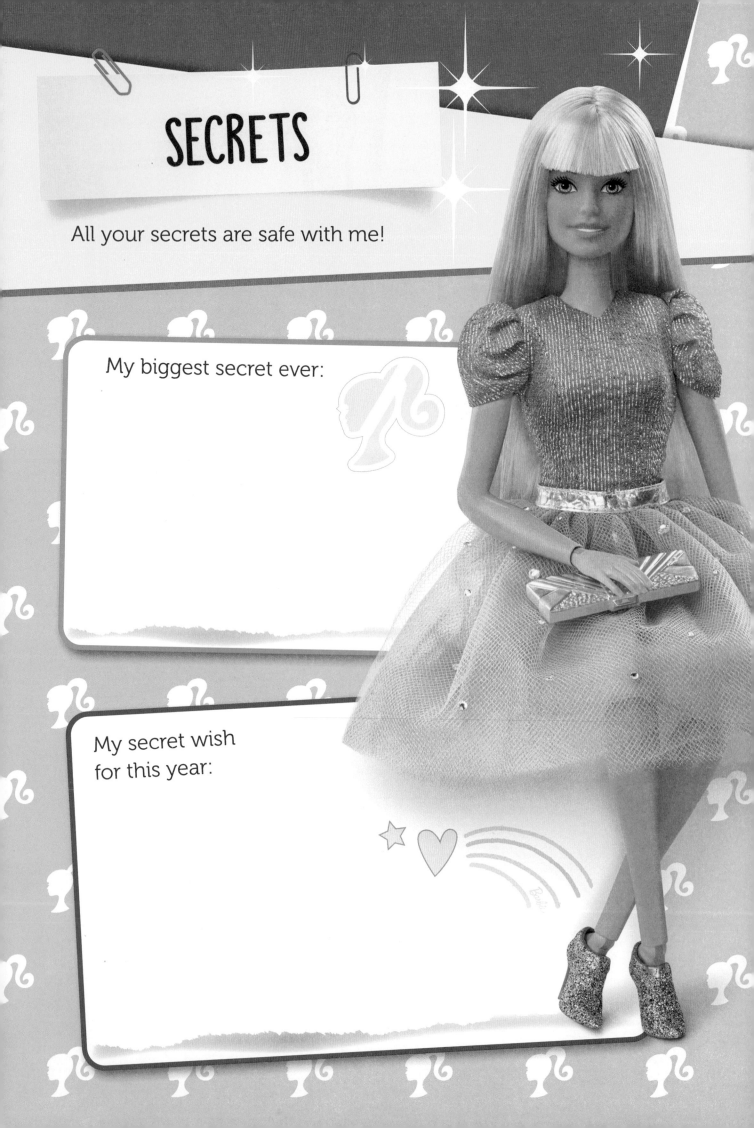

The secret I want to tell:

A secret I've shared:

My silliest secret ever:

FABULOUS FRIENDS

Even though we're all totally different, we're best friends and stick together through thick and thin. How would you describe your BFFs? Choose a word that really sums up each of your best friends.

COOL

KIND

FUNNY

SWEET

SMART

LOYAL

RUNWAY READY

ORGANISED

Tell us more about your friends by filling in their profiles.

Name: ....

Hair Colour: ....

Eye Colour: ....

Coolest Achievements: ....

What I like best about them: ....

Worst Habit: ....

Secret Crush: ....

Name: ....

Hair Colour: ....

Eye Colour: ....

Coolest Achievements: ....

What I like best about them: ....

Worst Habit: ....

Secret Crush: ....

Name: ....

Hair Colour: ....

Eye Colour: ....

Coolest Achievements: ....

What I like best about them: ....

Worst Habit: ....

Secret Crush: ....

Name: ....

Hair Colour: ....

Eye Colour: ....

Coolest Achievements: ....

What I like best about them: ....

Worst Habit: ....

Secret Crush: ....

PHOTO ALBUM

Glossify these pages with favourite photos of your friends!

BEST FRIENDS

The cool thing about having lots of best friends is that they are all great at different things. Whether you're chilling or out having fun, it's always better to be with a friend.

Which best friend has wicked style?

....

Who could be a vet?

....

Who's best at keeping secrets?

....

Who always cheers you up?

....

PARTY TIME

It's girls' night in! Plan a pinkerific sleepover with the girls.

Guest List:

....

....

....

....

....

Party Music:

....

....

....

....

Swap make-up secrets!

Sweet Snacks!

. . . .

. . . .

. . . .

. . . .

. . . .

Swap cute outfit plans!

Give each other new hairstyles!
Stick pictures here:

What secrets did you share?

. . . .

. . . .

. . . .

. . . .

. . . .

BFF BIRTHDAYS!

Keep a record of all the birthdays you need to remember here. It's great to keep a list so you can think of something luxe to make for an extra-special present and plan a fabulous party.

Name: ....
Birthday: ....
Age This Year: ....
Favourite Things: ....
Fab Gift Idea: ....

Name: ....
Birthday: ....
Age This Year: ....
Favourite Things: ....
Fab Gift Idea: ....

Name: ....
Birthday: ....
Age This Year: ....
Favourite Things: ....
Fab Gift Idea: ....

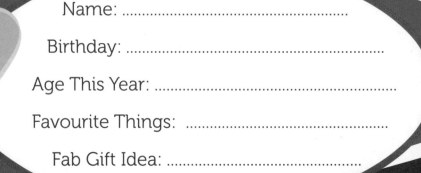

Name: ....

Birthday: ....

Age This Year: ....

Favourite Things: ....

Fab Gift Idea: ....

Name: ....

Birthday: ....

Age This Year: ....

Favourite Things: ....

Fab Gift Idea: ....

Name: ....

Birthday: ....

Age This Year: ....

Favourite Things: ....

Fab Gift Idea: ....

My Wish List!

Write a list of your top ten fabulous birthday presents:

....

....

....

....

....

FAMILY FILE

GOOD VIBES

KINDNESS ACTIVIST

I love being a big sister. Chelsea is so curious, and Stacie loves sports! Skipper is really into tech. What's your family like?

Who's the messiest?

....

Who's the funniest?

....

Who's good
at helping out?

....

What TV show could
your family star in?

....

Who makes things
for everyone?

....

BRAVE
BOLD   FEAR
LESS

Stick your coolest family photos here.

PRETTY PETS

My pets always make me feel happy. I love cuddling my cat Blissa and taking my dogs Taffy and Honey for walks. What pets do you have? If you don't have a pet, fill in the pet profile for your dream pet.

Animal Type: . . . .

Name: . . . .

Age: . . . .

Colours: . . . .

Attitude: . . . .

Cool Trick: . . . .

Favourite Food: . . . .

Cutest thing your pet has ever done:

. . . .

. . . .

Misty's the name of my favourite horse. What would your horse be called?

Stick a picture of your pet here!

SCHOOL STUFF

My friends make school one of the best places to be. What's school like for you?

Name of School: . . . .

Favourite Teacher: . . . .

Best Subject: . . . .

What do you wear? . . . .

Best mark ever: . . . .

If you were the head teacher, what would you change?

. . . .

. . . .

If you were a teacher, what would you teach?

. . . .

Best thing you've learned at school:

. . . .

Your school style can be just as awesome as your best look. Design a dream outfit for your school day.

FASHION SECRETS

Fill these pages with your trendy fashion tips and ideas for quick fixes.

What are your secret ways
to take an outfit from day to night?

....

....

....

What colour
accessories go with
all your outfits?

....

....

Which clothes
reflect your personality
the most?

....

....

....

....

....

Describe your best outfit
for meeting new people at parties!

....

What's your most
eye-catching hairstyle?

....

....

Which shoes make you walk like you're
on the runway?

....

....

FASHION FLAVOURS

What fashion items would you totally love to have? Cut out pictures from magazines and write a list of each season's must-haves!

Sassy tops   **Chunky belts**   Warm Colours

SPRING

Cool Jeans   **T-Shirts**   Fresh Colours

Wools and Knits

Lots of Layers

AUTUMN

Patterns and Prints   Headscarves

Chunky Scarves **Big Boots** Cool Coats

Rich Colours **Jumpers** Hot Hats

Cute Minis **Sunhats** Floaty Dresses

Sunglasses Flip Flops

SUMMER

STYLE ZONE

Signature colours and your favourite accessories are essential for individual style. Have you discovered your lucky colour? Check out the colours below and pick your top five.

COOL COLOURS

The colours you wear can totally change your mood. Power pink always makes me happy. Take a look at what these colours can do for you.

Pink

Pretty pink will always bring a glow to your cheeks; wear something pinkerific every day, like me!

Yellow

Can't make up your mind? A splash of yellow will help put you in a sunny mood.

Green

Green is a really creative colour, so wear it if you need tons of fresh ideas.

Purple

Put on some purple for a chill-out day. It's a calming colour for a cool mood.

Blue

Feel chilled and cool in blue. Wearing blue also helps people feel they can trust you.

Orange

A burst of orange picks you up if you're feeling a bit tired. It boosts your confidence too!

OUTFIT PLANNERS

Do you have a fabulous party, birthday or glittery event coming up? Plan four fantabulous outfits for your next big events by modelling them on me and my friends.

MAKE-UP MATCHMAKER

Experimenting with make-up helps keep my look fresh – it's really fun to change your style each season. Here are my secret palettes. Which shades would you wear together?

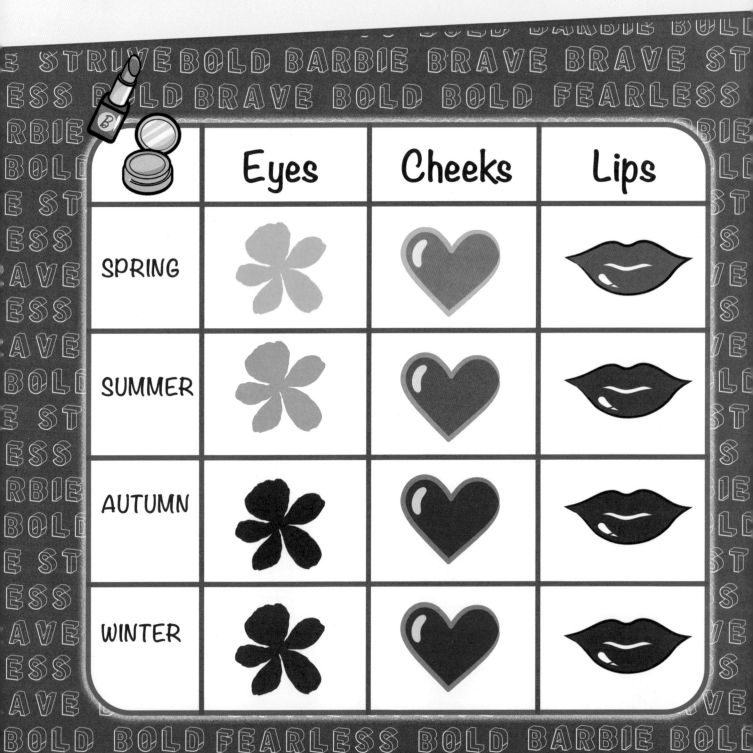

	Eyes	Cheeks	Lips
SPRING			
SUMMER			
AUTUMN			
WINTER			

HAIR HELPER

My hair changes with every outfit. Play around with your hair and add photos of the best styles below, then you can check out these pages every morning and know what will look fab!

WHAT'S UP IN JANUARY?

Favourite song of the month?

....

Favourite dance move of the month?

....

Favourite movie of the month?

....

Special place you visited:

....

....

Biggest news:

....

....

....

What parties did you go to?

....

....

Cute

Best book of the month:

....

Best BFF moment:

....

Favourite movie:

....

COOL

Top party:

....

New thing learned:

....

....

....

Favourite band of the month:

....

....

WHAT'S UP IN MARCH?

Best ever!

Best thing that has happened at school:

....

Favourite moment of the month:

....

Coolest website of the month:

....

Funniest thing that happened:

....

....

Hot style of the month:

....

....

Best accessories worn this month:

....

....

....

LOL

WHAT'S UP IN APRIL?

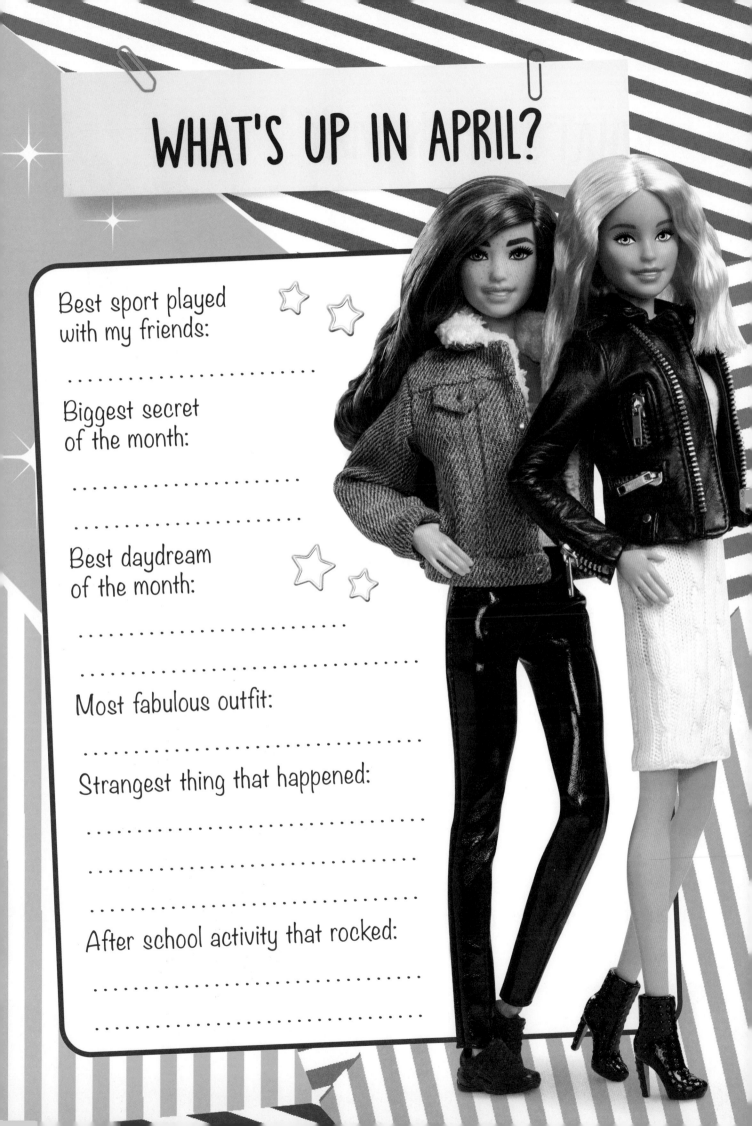

Best sport played
with my friends:

. . . .

Biggest secret
of the month:

. . . .

. . . .

Best daydream
of the month:

. . . .

. . . .

Most fabulous outfit:

. . . .

Strangest thing that happened:

. . . .

. . . .

. . . .

After school activity that rocked:

. . . .

WHAT'S UP IN MAY?

Favourite magazine of the month:

....

Best thing I drew:

....

Nicest thing I did for my family:

....

....

....

Quote of the month:

....

Coolest addition to my wardrobe:

....

....

Favourite pet moment of the month:

....

WHAT'S UP IN JUNE?

LOVE

BFFs forever!

Best sport played:

....

Favourite TV show:

....

Best meal I had this month:

....

Fabulous plans I made with friends:

....

....

....

Special night out moment with friends:

....

....

....

Shoes of the season:

....

....

WHAT'S UP IN JULY?

Cute!

Shopping!

Best beach moment:

. . . .

Must have fabric:

. . . .

Sunhat of choice:

. . . .

Best novel I read:

. . . .

Best friend moment to remember:

. . . .

. . . .

OMG

. . . .

Colour of the earrings bought in the month:

. . . .

. . . .

. . . .

WHAT'S UP IN AUGUST?

Cutest outfit of the month:

. . . .

Best place I went:

. . . .

. . . .

Favourite movie star of the month:

. . . .

Best story I read:

. . . .

Incredible bestie moment
to remember:

. . . .

. . . .

. . . .

The best clothes are from:

. . . .

. . . .

WHAT'S UP IN SEPTEMBER?

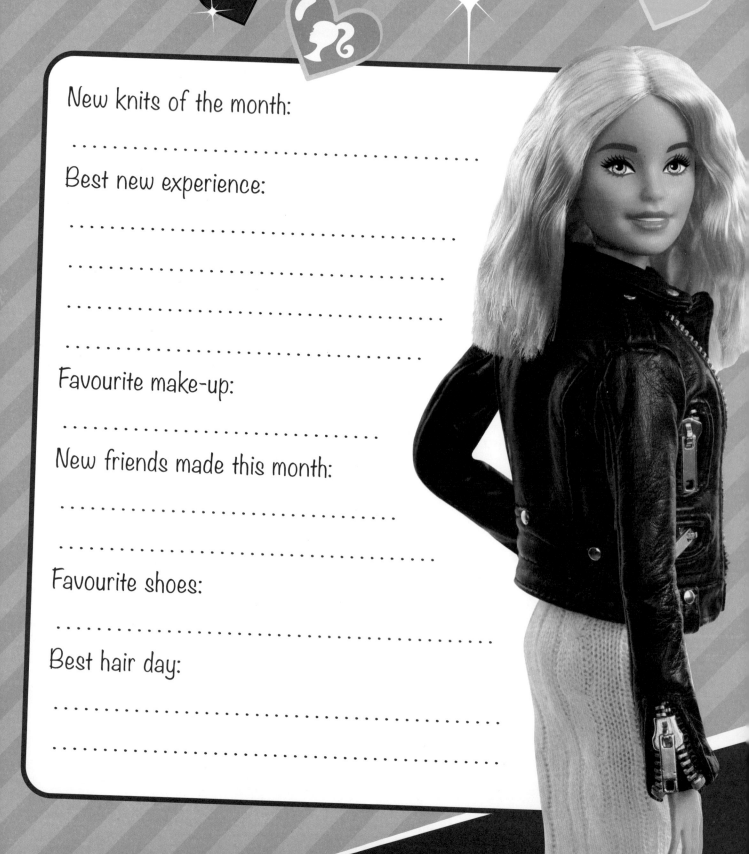

New knits of the month:

....

Best new experience:

....

....

....

Favourite make-up:

....

New friends made this month:

....

....

Favourite shoes:

....

Best hair day:

....

....

WHAT'S UP IN OCTOBER?

Funny **Adorable** **Scary**

Halloween costume:

....

Top party moment:

....

....

....

Best song of the month:

....

Favourite moment:

....

Best hair day:

....

Funniest quote of the month:

....

....

WHAT'S UP IN NOVEMBER?

Cute!

Most fabulous moment with friends:

....

....

....

Biggest event:

....

....

Best dance moves:

....

Favourite smoothie:

....

Most fabulous gift:

....

Super style!

Best sweatshirt:

....

....